THE one hundred greatest Cricketers